GUUUST!

NOW WE'RE TALKING! WE'LL *BLOW* PAST HIM IN NO TIME!

*ARRGH!* THIS IS *TOO* FAST! I CAN'T STOP!

Café

CLATTER!

ZOOM!

CRASH!

HUH? WHERE'D THIS COME FROM?

I'M FLYING!

GUST!

YIKES! I'M GOING *UP* IN THE WORLD!

WHOOSH!

HEY, LOOK! IT'S *MARY POPPINS!*

HAW-HAW! I'M NEARLY THERE! BERYL LOSES *AGAIN!*

SCHOOL

SCH

MIND IF I *POPPIN?*

OH, NO YOU DON'T! I'M GETTING THAT SEAT!

SLAM!

PARRRP!

OOPS! PARDON ME!

*URRGH!* THAT PONG'S TOO MUCH EVEN FOR *ME!*

BLITHER!

HEE-HEE! I KNEW I'D GET HERE FIRST WITH THE *WIND* BEHIND ME!

The Jocks and the Geordies in "Five-A-Side"

TAKE A LOOK AT THIS.

THERE'S FIVE OF US. WE SHOULD ENTER AN' WIN IT. IT'S ABOUT TIME WE WON SOMETHING AT FOOTBALL.

FIVE -A- SIDE FOOTBALL COMPETITION

FORGET IT. THAT TROPHY IS OURS.

IS THAT SO?

AYE, IT IS!

NOW, NOW, BOYS, LET'S BE CALM AND PLAY FAIR, IT'S ONLY FOOTBALL. LET'S SHAKE HANDS AND HAVE A GOOD GAME TOMORROW.

PLAY FAIR?

SHAKE HANDS?

COME ON NOW... SHAKE.

I SUPPOSE SO.

YOU'D BETTER NOT TELL ANYBODY ABOUT THIS!

GOOD... LUCK... HNNNGH!

SQUEEZE!

GNNGH! YOU TOO!

THAT WASN'T SO BAD, WAS IT?

DANNY SAID WE HAD TO PLAY FAIR...

...SO WE CHEAT LIKE MAD!

AYE!

RIGHT, LADS, WE NEED TO GET SOME TRAINING IN FOR THE BIG GAME.

BRAW. WE NEED TO HAMMER THE GEORDIES.

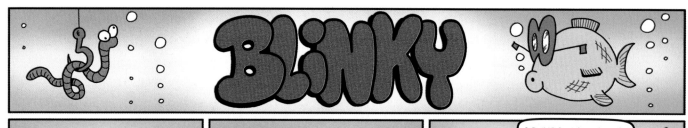

# DREADLOCK HOLMES

CAN'T BLAME ME FOR TRYIN'! I'M OFF FOR A STROLL TO TAKE MA MIND OFF YOUR WONDERFUL COOKING TILL TEATIME.

GOOD LUCK WITH THAT!

BEAUTIFUL DAY! AND NOT A CLOUD IN THE SKY.

ROSWELL 47miles

HUH? HOW COME IT'S JUST GONE DARK?

KE-RASH!

BLIPPLE! I NEED TO WORK ON MY LANDINGS!

BZZZT!

HOPEFULLY IT'LL TAKE OFF AGAIN WHEN MY MISSION IS OVER.

RUMBLE!

ZIBBLAT! NOT YET THOUGH - IT'S MOVING ON ITS OWN!

NOT QUITE...

WIBBLE! I'M OFF!

LEAP!

WHAT IN TARNATION IS THIS THING?!

PTOO!

# CUDDLES AND DIMPLES

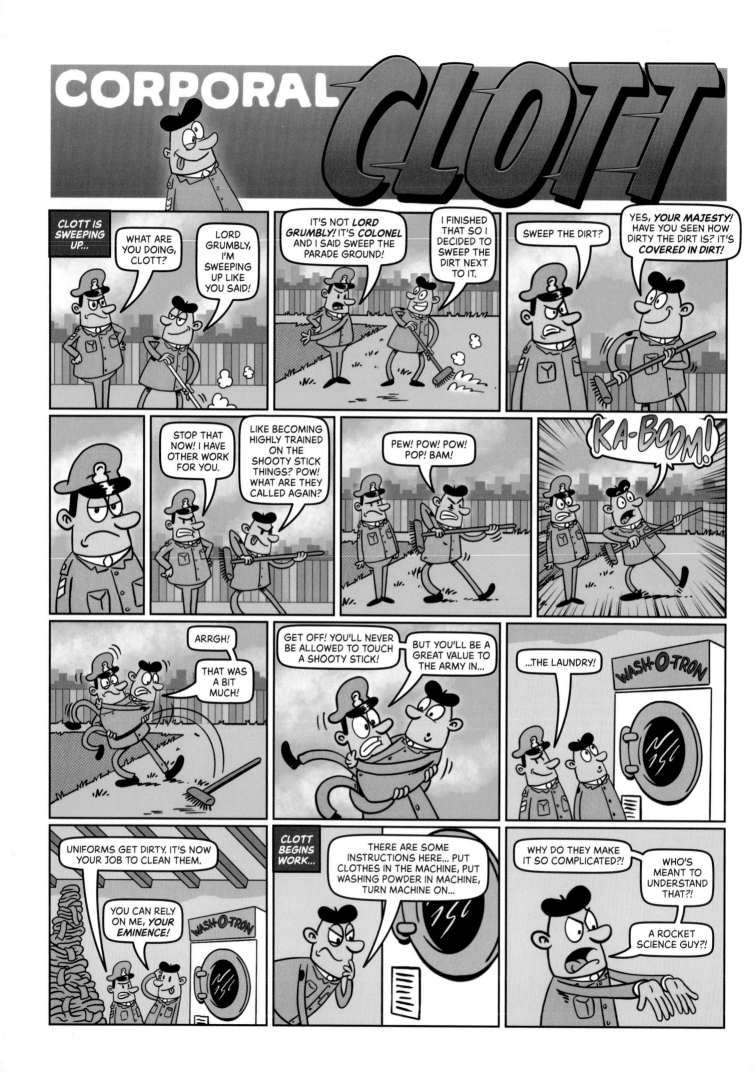

BUT...

ARRGH! I'VE JUST REALISED THE ENORMITY OF WHAT I'VE DONE! I'M JUST A CAT! I CAN'T HOST THE 2022 SNOW TRIALS!

TUT-TUT! BEING A CAT HASN'T STOPPED YOU DOING THINGS BEFORE, KORKY!

THOSE WERE SMALLER JOBS THOUGH, WINKER! AND THEY ALWAYS WENT WRONG WITH COMEDIC EFFECT!

THE TIME I WAS A FOOTBALL MANAGER WAS HILARIOUS, BUT DANDYTOWN FC WERE STILL RELEGATED!

RELAX! I'LL HELP!

PHEW! NOTHING EVER WENT WRONG WITH A PUBLIC SCHOOLBOY IN CHARGE!

WHAT SPORTS DO THE TRIALS HAVE? SNOWMAN BUILDING?

THE INTERNET SAYS ONE SPORT IS SPEED SKATING. HOW DO WE BUILD A SKATING, ER... TRACK?

IF WE BLOCK THE DRAINS ROUND THE ROUNDABOUT IN THE MIDDLE OF TOWN, POUR SOME WATER ON IT AND WAIT FOR IT TO FREEZE...

...AND DONE!

MAYBE THIS ISN'T GOING TO BE SO HARD AFTER ALL!

ARRGH! I CAN'T TURN!

SLIDE!

CLOSING OFF THE ROADS TO TRAFFIC MIGHT BE A GOOD IDEA!

SKID!
CRASH!
PRANG!
DINK!
BOSH!
RATTLE!

WHO WANTS TO DO SPEED SKATING?

ME!

NOT YOU! YOU SHOULDN'T EVEN BE IN THIS ANNUAL! SHOO!

BUT...

SHOVE!

HELLO! I'M YOUR HOST, WINKER WATSON! YOU'VE JOINED US FOR THE SPEED SKATING. THE COMPETITORS ARE LINED UP, WAITING FOR THE BEEP...

BEEP!

AND THEY'RE OFF! THREE OF THEM IN THE RIGHT DIRECTION!

WHOOSH!

IT LOOKS LIKE SKATING BEHIND SMASHER BRINGS EXTRA CHALLENGES!

GRR!

SMASH SMASH

OUT AHEAD IS BRASSNECK, THERE'S NOTHING IN THE RULES ABOUT TRANSFORMING YOURSELF INTO A ROCKET-POWERED SLEDGE!

ZOOM!

AND BRASSNECK WINS!

ROCKET!

ARRGH!

IT'S THE GOLD FOR BRASSNECK. BUT... WHERE IS HE?

1
2
3

HELP! I CAN'T STOP!

I'M SURE THAT ISN'T THE LAST WE'VE SEEN OF BRASSNECK!

NEXT UP IS THE SKI JUMP!

THERE ARE THE SKIS.

NO SIGN OF THEM JUMPING YET, BUT WE'LL STICK WITH THE, ER... ACTION.

THAT'S RIGHT, WINKER.

ANY MOMENT NOW THESE SKIS WILL JUMP. THE HIGHEST-JUMPING SKI WILL WIN THE GOLD MEDAL.

ANY MINUTE NOW. NOW! NOW?!

I'LL CHECK THE INTERNET AGAIN, I THINK WE'VE GONE WRONG SOMEWHERE.

SO...

WELCOME BACK TO THE SKI JUMP! FIRST UP IS CORPORAL CLOTT!

AT THE TOP...

I'M SCARED OF HEIGHTS, MR GRUMBLY!

HEIGHTS NEVER HURT ANYONE! IT'S THE LANDING THAT DOES THAT!

JUST REMEMBER WHAT I SAID.

'GET OUT OF MY BATH'?

IF YOU LAND FAR AWAY, THINK ABOUT STAYING THERE!

OH YEAH!

OFF I GO!

THERE MAY BE BETTER THINGS TO BUILD A SKI JUMP FROM THAN CARDBOARD! WHO KNEW?!

SHOOF!

CRASH!

FLUMP!

OOH! THAT'S UNLUCKY!

NEXT UP ON THE NEWLY-STRENGTHENED SKI JUMP IS DESPERATE DAN!

PHEW! MADE IT! YOU WOULDN'T BELIEVE HOW DIFFICULT THE JOURNEY FROM CACTUSVILLE WAS!

DAN'S GOING FOR IT!

WHEE!

THAT'S IMPRESSIVE, KORKY! LOOK AT HIM GO!

I DON'T WANT TO SAY DAN'S JUMP WILL WIN THE GOLD, BUT I'M STILL TALKING AND THERE'S STILL NO LANDING!

LOOK, DAD! BANANAMAN!

BACK IN CACTUSVILLE...

HOWDY, DAN! I THOUGHT YOU'D GONE TO DANDYTOWN?

SCRAPE!

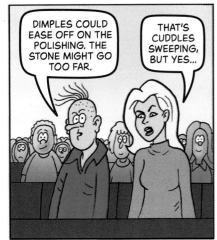

DIMPLES COULD EASE OFF ON THE POLISHING. THE STONE MIGHT GO TOO FAR.

THAT'S CUDDLES SWEEPING, BUT YES...

THAT STONE IS GOING *REALLY* FAST!

SHOVE!

CRASH!

UP AGAINST CUDDLES AND DIMPLES ARE POSTMAN PRAT AND KEYHOLE KATE!

SWEEP SWEEP

HOPEFULLY PRAT WILL BE ABLE TO *DELIVER* THE STONE TO ITS TARGET!

OOH, THAT'S UNLUCKY!

CRASH!

PARTICULARLY WHEN YOU CONSIDER THAT CUDDLES AND DIMPLES' DAD HAS GONE HOME!

HOW DID IT FIND ME?!

CRASH!

SORRY! I STILL CAN'T STOP!

I'M CONFUSED, KORKY. WHO WAS THE WINNER?

COMICS WERE THE WINNER, WINKER!

I'VE JUST REALISED THESE ARE ICE LOLLIES!

YUM! MICROPHONE FLAVOUR!

I'M BACK... GASP! DID I WIN?

WE'RE GOING TO TAKE A BREAK NOW, BUT WE'LL BE BACK LATER IN THE ANNUAL!

# DREADLOCK HOLMES

I LOVE DETECTIVE TV SHOWS! THEY'RE MY FAVOURITE!

I CAN REVEAL THAT THE CRIMINAL IS...

YOU'VE WATCHED TOO MUCH TV TODAY! TIME TO TURN IT OFF! WHY DON'T YOU READ A BOOK OR SOMETHING?

CLICK!

MUM! NOOOOO!

IT WAS THE END OF THE SHOW! THEY WERE ABOUT TO REVEAL WHO STOLE THE DIAMONDS!

DO SOMETHING ELSE! READ A BOOK FOR ONCE!

MUUUM!

I DON'T NEED TO WATCH THE END OF THE SHOW.

I CAN USE MY DETECTIVE SKILLS TO SOLVE THE CASE ON MY OWN!

SO... WHO STOLE THE DIAMONDS?

I HAVE NO IDEA! I NEED SOME HELP.

YOU CAN HELP ME, SNITCH! WHO'S A CLEVER, CRIME-SOLVING BOY? YOU ARE!

UH-OH!

I WILL BE THE GRUFF DETECTIVE WITH A MYSTERIOUS PAST.

YOU CAN BE THE COUNTESS WITH THE MISSING DIAMONDS.

WOOF?

SO, COUNTESS... TELL ME ABOUT THE NIGHT THE DIAMONDS WERE STOLEN.

WOOF, WOOF.

THE DIAMONDS WERE NEVER STOLEN, WERE THEY? YOU MADE THE WHOLE THING UP!

WOOF!

HAVING A TEA PARTY WITH YOUR DOG, ARE YOU, SHERMAN? HOW SWEET!

MARSHA! I'M TRYING TO SOLVE A CASE!

IF YOU WERE GOING TO STEAL PRICELESS DIAMONDS, WHERE WOULD YOU HIDE THEM?

I DUNNO, IN A TEAPOT?

NO, THEY SEARCHED THE TEAPOT BEFORE THE FIRST AD BREAK!

AD BREAK? IS THIS ABOUT THAT 'CRIMINAL CRIMES' TV SHOW YOU WATCH?

WHY DON'T YOU MESSAGE YOUR FRIENDS TO SEE IF ANY OF THEM WATCHED IT?

I DID! NONE OF THEM SAW IT!

WAIT! MY PHONE! I'VE HAD AN IDEA!

HELLO? IS THAT ITC TELEVISION? COULD YOU TELL ME WHO THE CRIMINAL WAS IN LAST NIGHT'S EPISODE OF 'CRIMINAL CRIMES'?

UH-HUH, YES, I SEE, THANK YOU.

WELL?

THEY TOLD ME NEVER TO CALL BACK AGAIN.

TELL ME ABOUT THE CASE, WHO ARE THE SUSPECTS?

THE THIEF WAS EITHER THE PROFESSIONAL FOOTBALLER OR THE ACTRESS!

OR MAYBE IT WAS THE RACE CAR DRIVER, OR THE BUTLER!

SHERMAN, THAT'S *BUTTER*, NOT THE BUTLER.

YOU'RE RIGHT, HE IS A *SLIPPERY* CUSTOMER. MAYBE HE DID IT?

ACTUALLY, FORGET IT, SEE YOU LATER.

I'LL USE A COMPUTER PROGRAM TO WORK THIS OUT.

IF I TYPE IN THE CRIMINALS FROM EVERY EPISODE OF 'CRIMINAL CRIMES', IT WILL WORK OUT WHO DID THIS ONE!

TYPE!

TYPE!

TYPE!

HERE'S THE ANSWER! THE CRIMINAL IS...

...'INTERNET CONNECTION PROBLEM'! *NOOOO!*

TO CATCH A CRIMINAL, I NEED TO THINK LIKE A CRIMINAL.

WHERE DOES MUM KEEP HER JEWELLERY?

WHAT ARE YOU DOING, SHERMAN? GET OUT!

BUT, MUM! I'LL NEVER SOLVE 'THE CASE OF THE COUNTESS'S DIAMONDS' NOW!

'THE CASE OF THE COUNTESS'S DIAMONDS'? THE *DETECTIVE* WAS THE CRIMINAL ALL ALONG!

WHAT? BUT HOW DID YOU KNOW?

I READ THE BOOK THAT THE TV EPISODE WAS BASED ON! I KEPT TELLING YOU TO READ A BOOK, BUT YOU DIDN'T LISTEN TO ME!

THE CASE OF THE COUNTESS'S DIAMONDS

AT BREAK TIME...

STATIONERY

WHERE'S BERYL GOT TO?

STATIONERY

PSST! CYNTH! GET IN HERE!

WHY ARE YOU HIDING IN THERE?

I'VE FIGURED IT ALL OUT, CYNTH! I'VE UNCOVERED THE TRUTH!

WHAT TRUTH?

SLAM!

IT ALL MAKES SENSE!

THE QUESTIONS, THE DISGUISE, THE MAGIC ALIEN FINGER...

...MR HOOMAN IS NOT HUMAN!

HE'S AN ALIEN!

YOU'RE STILL GOING ON ABOUT THIS ALIEN STUFF? I MEAN, MR HOOMAN IS A BIT WEIRD BUT HE IS A TEACHER AFTER ALL!

THAT'S WHAT HE WANTS YOU TO THINK, CYNTH! IT'S TIME TO WAKE UP AND SMELL THE ALIEN COFFEE!

YOU'RE ACTING WEIRDER THAN HIM, BERYL! YOU'LL BE PUTTING ON A TINFOIL HAT NEXT!

WAY AHEAD OF YOU! YOU CAN NEVER BE TOO SURE!

I'M OFF TO PLAY OUTSIDE. YOU CAN JOIN ME WHEN YOU'VE FINISHED BEING SILLY.

STATIONERY

YOU'LL SEE, CYNTHIA! YOU'LL ALL SEE!

HEAD

WHO'S BEEN MESSING WITH THE SCHOOL'S STATIONERY SUPPLIES?!

DETENTION FOR YOU BOTH! YOU'VE WRECKED THE STATIONERY CUPBOARD!

WE'RE GETTING TOO CLOSE TO THE TRUTH, THAT'S WHAT IT IS!

BUT I DIDN'T DO ANYTHING!

SO...

I MUST NOT WASTE SCHOOL SUPPLIES AND ALSO NOT RESIST THE IMMINENT ALIEN INVASION

WELL, HUMAN-CHILDS! AS PUNISHMENT FOR YOUR MISDEEDS YOU MUST WRITE OUT 'I MUST NOT WASTE SCHOOL SUPPLIES AND ALSO NOT RESIST THE IMMINENT ALIEN INVASION' ONE HUNDRED TIMES!

TELL ME YOU HEARD THAT STUFF ABOUT AN ALIEN INVASION! C'MON, CYNTH! WHAT MORE PROOF DO YOU NEED?

MAYBE HE'S JUST JOKING WITH US?

I AM JUST LEAVING TO GO AND DO SOMETHING VERY HUMAN-LIKE, SUCH AS IMBIBING SOME BOILED TEA LEAVES FROM A MUG. YOU TWO CARRY ON!

# CORPORAL CLOTT

The Jocks and the Geordies in NICEST

THAT OLD DEAR IS STRUGGLING WITH HER SHOPPING.

I BET THEM JOCKS MAKE FUN OF HER.

THAT'S A LOAD OF SHOPPING. DO YOU NEED A HAND CARRYING IT?

I DO, ACTUALLY. I BOUGHT MORE THAN I PLANNED.

JUST YOU RELAX AND WE'LL SEE TO THAT.

THAT'S SO KIND.

YOU'RE SUCH LOVELY BOYS. I CAN'T IMAGINE WHY EVERYONE SAYS YOU'RE TROUBLEMAKERS LIKE THAT MOB OF GEORDIES YOU FIGHT WITH.

WE'RE NICE LADS, MISSUS. THEY ALWAYS CAUSE TROUBLE FOR US.

DID YOU HEAR THAT, LADS? WE'RE NICER THAN THE GEORDIES.

WE KNEW THAT ANYWAY.

I'M NOT HAVING THAT. IT'S NOT ON. WE ARE GOING TO PROVE TO EVERYBODY THAT WE ARE NICER THAN THAT BUNCH OF JOCKS.

HOW ARE WE GONNA DO THAT, LIKE?

SO...

MR BROWNLEE, YOU TAKE A SEAT AND WE'LL GO AND DO YOUR SHOPPING FOR YOU AND DELIVER IT TO YOUR HOUSE.

THAT'S FAIR DECENT OF YOU, LADS.

AND...

HERE YOU GO, MR BROWNLEE. PITY WE DIDN'T KNOW YOU ONLY SHOP ONCE A YEAR.

I'M SHATTERED.

YOU AREN'T THE BUNCH OF ROUGH HORRORS I EXPECTED. YOU'RE EVEN NICER THAN THOSE JOCK LADS WHO HELPED MRS BOGGS.

AT THE JOCKS' HUT...

THE OLD FELLA SAID WHAT?

APPARENTLY, THE GEORDIES ACTED EVEN NICER THAN WE DID.

WE OUGHT TO BELT THEM RIGHT UP THE HOOTER FOR BEING NICER THAN US!

BEING NICER THAN US? WHAT A DIRTY ROTTEN TRICK. WE WILL GO OUT THERE AND BE EVEN NICER TO MORE PEOPLE!

WHETHER THEY LIKE IT OR NOT!

BUNCH OF SCOUNDRELS.

LATER...

COME ON, LADS. SMILES ON. LET'S BE NICE.

AYE, WE'RE REALLY NICE, US.

NEARBY...

YOUNG PEOPLE TODAY...

ARE THERE ANY NICE ONES LEFT?

MY GARDEN'S OVERGROWN. I CAN'T DEAL WITH IT MYSELF ANY MORE.

DID YOU HEAR THAT, BOYS?

AYE, WE DID.

GENTLEMEN, WE COULDN'T HELP OVERHEARING YOUR GARDEN PROBLEM AND WE ARE THE LADS TO HELP.

THAT WOULD BE KIND OF YOU.

THAT'S THE GARDEN THERE.

Old Boot community PLOT.

DON'T YOU WORRY, WE CAN DEAL WITH IT.

ARE YOU HAVIN' A LAUGH?!

IT'LL TAKE ALL DAY!

LOOK AT HOW MUCH WORK THAT WILL BE.

AYE, LADS, BUT IT'LL BE WORTH IT TO SHOW THE GEORDIES THAT WE'RE NICER THAN THEM.

AYE, I SUPPOSE SO.

I'LL WATER THE FLOWERS.

GOOD LAD.

URRGH!

NO!

TURN IT OFF!

I'LL TRIM THIS HEDGE.

GOOD IDEA.

THIS IS NICE AND RELAXING, THIS.

SNIP!

SNIP!

PECK!

PECK!

OW! GET OFF! ME AND MY BIG MOUTH!

IT MUST HAVE BEEN NESTING IN THERE.

I WISH IT HAD STAYED IN BED. I WISH *I'D* STAYED IN BED TOO.

WE'RE GETTING THE JOB DONE. I JUST NEED TO GET THIS MOWER GOING.

THERE! IT WORKS.

WE NOTICED.

KEEP GOING, YOU'RE DOING A GREAT JOB THERE.

THANKS VERY MUCH.

WHAT A SPLENDID JOB, ISN'T IT NICE TO SEE PEOPLE BEING HELPFUL INSTEAD OF FIGHTING?

YOU'VE DONE A CRACKING JOB, MUCH BETTER THAN THE GEORDIES WOULD HAVE DONE.

WE'VE GOT A SURPRISE FOR YOU AS A TREAT.

DID YOU HEAR THAT? WE WERE BETTER THAN THE GEORDIES AND WE'RE GETTING A TREAT. WILL IT BE ICE CREAM? CASH?

THANKS FOR DOING UP MY GRANDAD'S GARDEN, BOYS. THAT'S PROPER NICE.

YOU CONNED US INTO DOING THIS!

YOU... YOU BUNCH OF...

I CAN'T BELIEVE YOU FELL FOR THE OLDEST TRICK IN THE BOOK! HA-HA!

OOF!

OW!

OOFYAH!

I THOUGHT YOU SAID YOUR LOT WERE NICE.

I THOUGHT YOU SAID YOUR LOT WERE NICE.

I LANDED A NICE UPPERCUT.

THAT LEFT HOOK WAS NICER, OW!

# KEYHOLE KATE

OOH... WHAT SECRETS ARE THROUGH THIS KEYHOLE? I SEE... BOOKS! AND... PENS!

OF COURSE YOU DO, KATE! THAT'S THE SCHOOL STORE CUPBOARD! NOW STOP SNOOPING AND PAY ATTENTION TO THE LESSON!

BAH! YES, SIR!

I HAVE A SPECIAL ASSIGNMENT FOR YOU, KATE! LET'S SEE IF YOU CAN TELL THE CLASS A STORY THAT *DOESN'T* INVOLVE KEYHOLES!

GASP!

ERM... LET ME THINK... THIS IS THE STORY OF *SPACE KATE*, GIRL ASTRONAUT!

GOOD START, KATE! THERE ARE NO KEYHOLES IN SPACE!

**SPACE KATE** WAS IN DEEP SPACE, EXPLORING A STRANGE PLANET.

THE PLANET WAS RULED BY EVIL ROBOTS WHO TOOK SPACE KATE AS THEIR PRISONER!

BUT SHE USED, ER... A *MAGIC WAND* TO FREE THE OTHER PRISONERS...

... AND THE PEOPLE DEFEATED THE ROBOTS AND PEACE WAS RESTORED TO THE PLANET!

*EXCELLENT*, KATE! YOU DIDN'T MENTION KEYHOLES ONCE! HAVE A SPECIAL CERTIFICATE!

HA-HA! GOOD JOB TEACHER COULDN'T SEE INTO MY IMAGINATION!

Certificate for Best Story

BY THE WAY, WHAT WAS THE NAME OF YOUR STORY?

PLANET KEYHOLE-TOPIA AND THE KEY TO DEFEATING THE KEYHOLE-SHAPED ROBOTS!

WHAT??!

Certificate for Best Story

I'LL HAVE THAT BACK!

SIGH. I MADE A *KEY MISTAKE* THERE!

# CUDDLES AND DIMPLES

# BLINKY

YAY! A FUN-FILLED DAY AT ACTIVITY WORLD!

THIS IS GOING TO BE FAB!

ENQUIRIES

PHEW! ONE MORE RACK AND WE'LL HAVE FINISHED REORGANISING ALL TEN THOUSAND BOOKS IN THE LIBRARY.

I'M LOOKING FOR FUN.

THAT'S OVER HERE, YOUNG MAN.

HUMOUR

NO, THANK YOU...

...I'LL SAVE THE CLIMBING WALL UNTIL LATER.

I'LL DO THE TRAMPOLINE FIRST, I THINK!

FLYING FOR BEGINNERS

BOING!

FLAP! FLAP! FLAP!

WAAH!

FLAP! FLAP! FLAP!

MEGA BOUNCE!

WHAT NEXT?

OH YEAH?

YEAH!

A SPOT OF BEAR WRESTLING DOES NO HARM EITHER.

SAME TIME AGAIN NEXT WEEK, PAL?

YOU KNOW WHERE TO FIND ME, DAN!

DAB! DAB!

DUST! DUST!

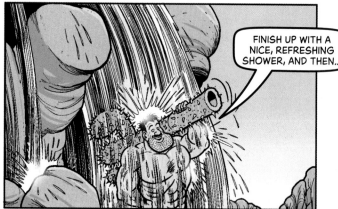

FINISH UP WITH A NICE, REFRESHING SHOWER, AND THEN...

...BACK HOME FOR A GOOD OL' COW PIE, AH'M FAMISHED!

JUST IN TIME, UNCLE DAN. CAN YOU OPEN UP THIS JAR OF PICKLES?

HA-HA! SINCE WHEN DID YOU START ASKIN' SILLY QUESTIONS?

NNNNNNNNGH! MMMMMMMMM! NNNNNNNGGHHHHRRRRRRRRR!

YA BIG GALOOT! GIVE IT HERE.

BRIGHTY

THERE NOW, DINNER'S READY, BOYS.

SHUCKS! AH MUST HAVE LOOSENED IT.

BEAM!

TWIST!

WHAT DID HE SAY HIS NAME WAS?

IT'S OKAY, I HAVE AN APPOINTMENT.

THAT'S A FUNNY NAME.

AH, SPACE RAOUL! ON TIME AS USUAL!

YOUR HIGHNESS, KING FLOBBLE OF FLOBBLETON-7.

I'M JUST SORRY I WASN'T HERE SOONER.

YOU SAID YOU HAD LOST SOMETHING VALUABLE, AND THAT I'M THE ONLY ONE WHO CAN BRING IT BACK TO YOU!

INDEED.

MY FAVOURITE CROWN...IT HAS BEEN STOLEN!

GASP! WHAT A DASTARDLY ACT!

HOWEVER, THE THIEF LEFT BEHIND A CURIOUS SPARKLY RESIDUE.

IN FACT...

...I THINK I'VE SEEN THIS BEFORE!

YOU WERE RIGHT TO CALL ME OUT, SIRE. I AM JUST THE RIGHT SPACE CAPTAIN TO SOLVE THE CRIME FOR YOU!

OH, BUT I ALREADY KNOW WHO THE THIEF IS...

..AFTER ALL, YOU LEFT A CONFESSION!

Hello!
It was me, SPACE RAOUL, who stole your crown!
Signed, me
(Space Raoul)

UH.

OH.

ONE CRASH-LAND LATER...

NOOOO!

HOW COULD LIFE BE SO CRUEL TO TAKE YOU AWAY FROM ME?

SIR?

MY PORTRAIT, QUIBBLE!

THE CRASH SCUFFED MY HANDSOME PORTRAIT!

 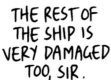

I WILL NEVER SMILE AGAIN.

THE REST OF THE SHIP IS VERY DAMAGED TOO, SIR.

MY BEAUTIFUL SHIP, ALL DIRTY AND RUINED ON SOME WEIRD ALIEN PLANET. WHAT ELSE COULD POSSIBLY GO WRONG?

SCHLUCK!!

OH!

OH, THAT FEELS DISGUSTING.

LAWKS! LOOK, QUIBBLE! IT'S THE PLOP-PLOPS, ALIEN INHABITANTS OF THE PLANET GAARP!

I'VE CRASH-LANDED HERE BEFORE! I KNOW WHERE WE ARE!

OOH. THERE DO SEEM TO BE A LOT OF THEM.

UMM, SIR?

ARE WE BEING CAPTURED?

SOMETIMES IT'S VERY HARD TO KNOW, QUIBBLE.

OH! THEY'VE BROUGHT US TO THEIR SACRED TEMPLE, WHERE THEY KEEP THE PRICELESS STATUE OF THEIR DEITY...LADY PLOP-PLOP!

# CORPORAL CLOTT

COLONEL GRUMBLY IS WELCOMING THE NEW RECRUITS...

WELCOME TO THE ARMY, I'LL BE TAKING YOU THROUGH THE BASIC...

URRGH! LOOK AT THEM!

LOOK! IT'S DREEB THE ALIEN FROM BERYL THE PERIL!

THIS SHOULD BE EASIER THAN BEING A TEACHER.

THIS IS CORPORAL CLOTT. HE'LL BE TAKING YOU THROUGH BASIC TRAINING.

CLOTT IS LEFT TO TRAIN THE RECRUITS...

ER... WHAT WAS BASIC TRAINING LIKE? IT WAS AGES AGO, I CAN'T REALLY REMEMBER TUESDAY. TRAINING WAS MOSTLY SHOUTING I THINK...

OKAY, YOU SILLY BILLYS! DROP AND GIVE ME TWENTY!

BOO-HOO! WAAH!

WHAT'S THE MATTER?

YOU CALLED HIM SILLY!

DON'T YOU THINK THAT'S A BIT HARSH?!

SNIFF!

WHEN I WENT THROUGH BASIC TRAINING, I WAS CALLED SILLY BILLY ALL THE TIME AND IT NEVER DID ME ANY HARM! EXCEPT IT WAS QUITE HURTFUL AND UPSET ME A LOT. WHAT I'M TRYING TO SAY IS I'M SORRY!

I THINK YOU'RE ALL LOVELY PEOPLE. NOW DROP AND GIVE ME 20.

PLEASE.

20 WHAT?

I...

...DON'T...

...KNOW.

20 POUNDS?

20 SWEETS?

20 *PUPPIES?*

AW! PLEASE LET IT BE PUPPIES!

I DON'T HAVE ONE PUPPY!

YOU CAN OWE ME THE PUPPIES. THE NEXT BIT OF BASIC TRAINING I REMEMBER WAS RUNNING THROUGH THE PLAYGROUND.

ISN'T IT CALLED AN ASSAULT COURSE?

Panel 1: WELL IF YOU WANT TO GIVE IT ITS FANCY LA-DI-DA NAME! JUST LEG IT!

Panel 2: THE NEW RECRUITS SET OFF...

FLOAT!

A SIMPLE ENOUGH CHALLENGE.

Panel 3: ISN'T FLYING AGAINST THE RULES?

THERE'S NOTHING IN THE RULE BOOK ABOUT FLYING.

THAT'S A *COLOURING IN BOOK!*

Panel 4: IN THE NEXT PART OF BASIC TRAINING I REMEMBER WE HAD TO TAKE SOMETHING TO BITS AND PUT IT BACK TOGETHER. NOW, WHAT WAS IT?

A WEAPON? - ED

Panel 5: A VACUUM CLEANER!

Panel 6: SO...

OKAY, NOW PUT THEM BACK TOGETHER.

ER...

HOW?

WOW!

Panel 7: NOW, LET'S SEE IF THEY WORK.

ERM, CORPORAL CLOTT...

LET'S SEE HOW WELL THIS 'CLEANS' AND BY CLEANS I MEAN...

Panel 8: BA-ZOINK!!!

MOST EFFECTIVE!

Panel 9: MR GRUMBLY!

SUFFERING SERGEANTS! CLOTT, YOU CAMO'ED CLOWN! WHAT ARE YOU TEACHING THEM?!

BEANO

Panel 10: NOTHING! I MEAN NOT THAT! ONE RECRUIT JUST KNOWS HOW TO DO EXTRA STUFF!

WELL GET RID OF THEM!

AND HAVE YOU SEEN MY FAVOURITE TANK? I CAN'T REMEMBER WHERE I PARKED IT.

WATCH OUT FOR DREEB IN BLINKY LATER. - ED

# CUDDLES AND DIMPLES

I'M GOING TO HELP MUM IN THE GARDEN.

I DOUBT THAT!

YOU CAN FEED THE TOMATO PLANTS.

OKEY-DOKEY.

HERE WE GO.

Plant Food

Paint

I LOVE TOMATOES, THEY'RE *SOUP*-ER!

EEK!

SPLOOP!

TRY PRUNING THIS HEDGE.

EASY, I'M A *TOP* TOPIARIST.

A LITTLE BIT OFF HERE... A LITTLE BIT OFF THERE...

SNIP!

SNIP!

SNIP! SNIP! SNIP!

...I'M A *CUT* ABOVE THE REST!

SNIP!

PERHAPS MOWING THE LAWN WOULD BE SAFER.

IT'LL BE A *PUSHOVER*.

OOF! THIS IS HARD WORK!

WE ALWAYS SAID YOU LOT WERE RUBBISH AND WE'VE JUST PROVED IT!

COME BACK SO WE CAN MARMALISE YOU!

GET LOST, YA LOSERS!

LET US IN, I'VE GOT A BUNCH OF FIVES WI' YOUR NAME ON IT!

YOU'LL NEVER GET IN, WE'VE GOT THE BEST HUT FOR MILES AROUND.

YOUR SHED'S A DUMP, MAN, A DUMP!

WHAT DID HE SAY?

DID HE CALL OUR BONNIE WEE HUT A DUMP?

AYE, HE DID.

WE'LL SEE ABOUT THAT. IF HE WANTS TO SEE A DUMP WE'LL SHOW HIM ONE.

NEARBY...

WE NEED TO GET REVENGE ON THEM JOCKS.

WHAT HAVE THEY DONE TO OUR HUT?

NOW THAT'S WHAT I CALL A DUMP!

LADS, I'VE GOT AN IDEA, GATHER ROUND.

THE NEXT DAY...

COME ON, LADS, WE'LL GIVE THAT HUT OF THEIRS ANOTHER GOING OVER.

BUT...

BIG JOCK! THEY'VE BEEN BUSY!

FORT GEORDIES

# BERYL the PERIL

AH! IT'S NICE AND QUIET AROUND HERE TODAY!

SPORT

DANDY NEWS

DAD INDULGES IN OMINOUS FORESHADOWING

I MEAN, IT'S *REALLY* QUIET...

...A BIT *TOO* QUIET.

DAAAAAAAD!

WAAH! BERYL!

SPORT

R!!!P!

CAN I GET THIS NEW GAMES CONSOLE? CAN I? CAN I? PLEEEEEAASE!

GAMEBOX 5

NEW! £599

£599?! WHAT'S WRONG WITH YOUR GAMEBOX 4?!

PFFT! THAT'S SO *LAST GEN*, DAD, THE GAMEBOX 5 HAS 12 TERAFLOPS, NATIVE 4K RESOLUTION AND A SUPER-FAST SSD!

WHAT DOES THAT EVEN MEAN? ISN'T A TERAFLOP A TYPE OF DINOSAUR?

I REMEMBER WHEN COMPUTER GAMES CAME ON A CASSETTE! YOU'D HAVE TO WAIT A DAY AND A HALF FOR THEM TO LOAD, SOMETIMES YOU'D HAVE TO TAKE A PENCIL AND WIND THE TAPE BACK IN...

OH NO! DAD'S STARTED REMINISCING!

SO CAN I GET IT, THEN?

*NO!* IT'S NEARLY £600! WHAT AM I, MADE OF MONEY? MAKE YOUR OWN ENTERTAINMENT! IT'S FREE!

OKAY THEN, I WILL. HEH-HEH-HEH!

# DREADLOCK HOLMES

I FINALLY FINISHED TIDYING MY BEDROOM! IT TOOK ME ALL MORNING, BUT NOW I CAN SEE SOME FRIENDS.

MUM! MY ROOM IS TIDY! I'M GOING OUT NOW.

SLAM!

IS IT REALLY? I'LL BE THE JUDGE OF THAT.

YES, IT IS! I SPENT ALL MORNING, AND NOW IT LOOKS LIKE...

A COMPLETE MESS!

NICE TRY! YOU'RE NOT GOING OUT UNTIL THIS ROOM IS CLEAN!

I DON'T GET IT! I JUST TIDIED!

NOBODY COULD'VE GOT PAST ME INTO THE ROOM.

IT'S A LOCKED ROOM MYSTERY! THE LATEST CASE FOR DREADLOCK HOLMES!

ARE YOU TIDYING YOUR ROOM?

NEARLY!

I'M GOING TO LOOK FOR CLUES IN THE MESS. I CAN'T TIDY UP UNTIL I DO THAT!

AHA! A CLUE! THIS PEN DEFINITELY BELONGS TO MY SISTER!

MARSHA! I HAVE EVIDENCE THAT...

MY PINK PEN! YOU'RE FINALLY GIVING IT BACK AFTER YOU BORROWED IT!

I DID?

YEAH, I THINK YOU WERE USING IT TO TICKLE SNITCH.

HEE-HEE-HEE!

OH YEAH! THAT WAS PRETTY FUN!

ON SECOND THOUGHTS, I DON'T WANT THIS BACK. WAS THERE ANYTHING ELSE?

DID YOU MESS UP MY ROOM THIS MORNING?

I'VE BEEN IN MY ROOM ALL MORNING AND YOU'VE BEEN IN YOUR ROOM.

HOW COULD I HAVE DONE THAT?

THESE ARE MY CURRENT THEORIES ABOUT HOW SOMEONE GOT INTO MY ROOM.

I'M GLAD YOU ASKED!

MAYBE YOU USED A COMPLICATED PULLEY SYSTEM TO STICK TO THE CEILING?

I DIDN'T GET ON THE GYMNASTICS TEAM, REMEMBER?

MAYBE YOU USED AN INVISIBILITY CLOAK?

SHERMAN, THOSE ONLY EXIST IN THOSE WIZARD BOOKS YOU READ.

DID YOU USE A TELEPORTER?

NO, BECAUSE I DON'T LIVE IN A SCIENCE FICTION MOVIE.

MAYBE YOU DIDN'T DO IT THEN, MARSHA.

SNITCH! DID YOU MESS UP MY ROOM?

WOOF!

DID YOU HIDE IN MY CUPBOARD AND THEN JUMP OUT LATER?

WOOF.

# WELCOME BACK TO...
# Dandytown SNOW TRIALS PART 2!

KORKY! WAKE UP! KORKY! THEY'RE BACK!

COMICS, WE'RE WINKER COMICS! ZZZZZZ.

YUM! MICROPHONE FLAVOUR! ZZZZ.

WHO?! I'M AWAKE! I'M AWAKE! OH, WINKER! I HAD A TERRIBLE DREAM! I DREAMT I WAS IN CHARGE OF THE 2022 SNOW TRIALS! IT'S RIDICULOUS NOW THAT I'M AWAKE BUT IT FELT SO REAL AT THE TIME!

IT *IS* REAL! IT'S HAPPENING NOW!

WHAT?!

WHAT DO WE DO? WE NEED TO THINK OF MORE SPORTS! CRICKET! CRICKET'S A SPORT!

IT'S NOT A WINTER SPORT!

YOU'RE JUST BEING PICKY!

OKAY, WE'LL DO SNOWMANNING!

AFTERNOON, READERS! YOU JOIN US AT A CRITICAL POINT - THE FINALS!

IT'S NECK AND NECK AS BERYL AND GREEDY PIGG ADD THE FINISHING TOUCHES TO...

CRASH!!

WINKER! WHAT HAVE YOU DONE?!

SNOWMANNING ISN'T A SPORT! BUT BOBSLEIGH IS!

THERE'S THE SLEIGH... BUT WHERE'S BOB? WHO'S BOB?

I KNOW A DOG CALLED BOB.

COMPETING AGAINST ONE ANOTHER ARE BULLY BEEF AND CHIPS!

HAW-HAW!

DOOOSH!

JAM!

DEAR, OH DEAR! LOOK AT THAT!

BEND!!

LOOK AT WHAT?

SLAP!

THIS!

STOP! STOP! STOP, YOU TWO! YOU'RE MEANT TO STAND ON THOSE BOARDS, SLIDE AROUND AND DO TRICKS!

WE'RE NOT DOING THAT! IT SOUNDS DANGEROUS!

YES! WE MIGHT HURT OURSELVES!

BUT... BUT...

...NEXT UP - ALPINE SKIING!

WE'LL BE DOING THE SLALOM!

GET IN! I LOVE A BIT OF SALMON!

SLALOM.

SALMON?

SLA-LOM!

SALMON!

SLALOM IS WHERE YOU SKI DOWN A WIGGLY COURSE IN BETWEEN LOTS OF FLAGS.

AND YOU WIN A LOVELY BIG FISH?

THERE'S NO FISH,

YOU KEEP YOUR FLAGS, I'M HAVING THIS FISH!

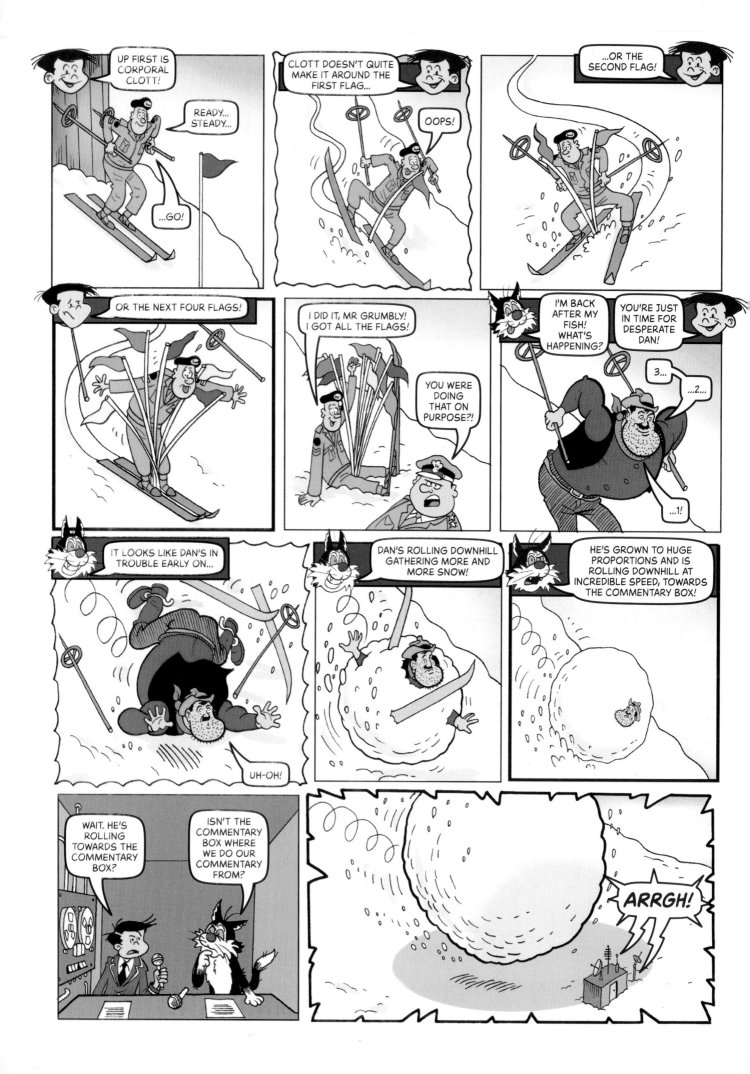

# FACE THE MUSIC!

BERYL'S BEEN MOVING THINGS AROUND IN THE MUSIC SHOP! CAN YOU SPOT TEN THINGS SHE'S CHANGED?

Tick 'em off as you find them!

SOLUTION

TRAINING STARTS...

WE'LL START ON THE RIFLE RANGE.

I GET A SHOOTY STICK?!

NO, HE DOES NOT! NEVER GIVE CLOTT ANYTHING LIKE THAT!

BUT HE'S A SOLDIER.

EXCITED!

GIVE HIM A MOP AND YOU'LL SEE!

HALF A SECOND LATER...

OW! MY EYE!

I'LL LEAVE YOU TO IT.

CAPTAIN SJ! THE WET END'S ON FIRE!

SO...

CLOTT, NO!

ZZZZZZ!

NO, CLOTT!

CLOTT, NO!

NO!!!

LATER...

AHH! THIS IS BETTER.

WHERE'S CLOTT?

IN THE BRIG. I LOCKED HIM UP BECAUSE NO-ONE CAN BE THAT STUPID. HE'S CLEARLY AN ENEMY AGENT.

HE'S HAPPY. I'LL LEAVE HIM IN THERE A WHILE.

MY OWN ROOM! THIS MUST BE A REWARD FOR ALL MY GOOD ARMYING!

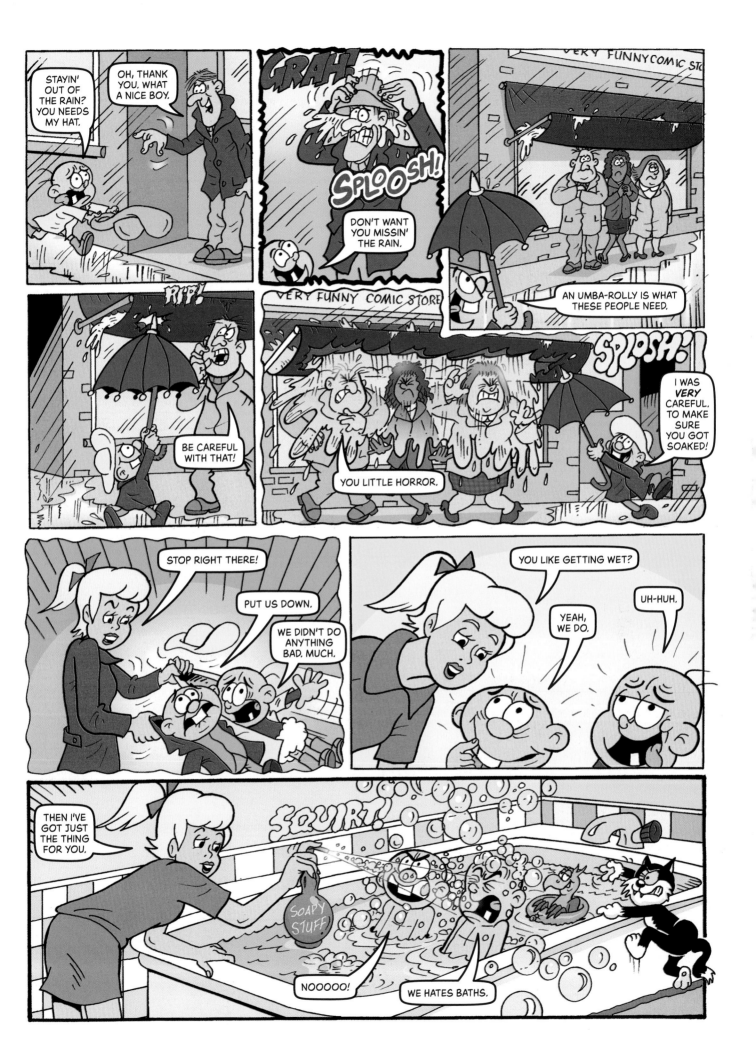

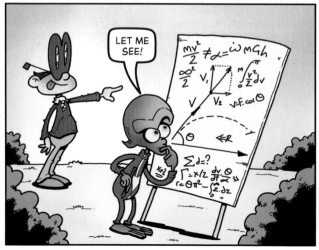

# DREADLOCK HOLMES

I LOVE CHRISTMAS! BECAUSE OF MY BRILLIANT POWERS OF DEDUCTION, I'VE BOUGHT THE BEST PRESENTS FOR EVERYONE.

THIS MAGNIFYING GLASS IS FOR MY SISTER, BECAUSE WHO WOULDN'T WANT THAT?

THIS 'BIG BOOK OF DETECTIVE STORIES' IS FOR MY MUM, MAYBE SHE'LL LET ME BORROW IT?

BIG BOOK OF DETECTIVE STORIES

THIS COOL NEW DEERSTALKER HAT IS FOR MY DOG, SNITCH.

I'LL JUST WEAR IT FOR NOW.

YET AGAIN MY SUPERIOR INTELLECT WINS CHRISTMAS!

WAIT A MINUTE! I CAN'T DETECT ANY PRESENTS FOR ME UNDER THE TREE!

CALM DOWN, MASTER DETECTIVE! HERE'S YOUR PRESENT FROM ME!

LET ME SEE!

HEY! DON'T OPEN IT YET! IT'S NOT CHRISTMAS UNTIL TOMORROW!

I'M A MASTER DETECTIVE! I DON'T NEED TO OPEN THIS PRESENT TO FIND OUT WHAT IT IS!

I WILL DEDUCE IT INSTEAD!

GRAB!

'HIS OLD DIVING GEAR MADE THE PERFECT SPACESUIT.'

TIME FOR TAKE-OFF.

DON'T FORGET TO WRITE!

'5...4... 3... 2... 1! WE HAVE LIFT OFF!'

BRING ME BACK SOME ROCK!

SURE WILL - SEE YOU NEXT WEEK!

'AND SOON... THE MOON!'

YEE-HAW!

FWOOOOOSH!

THAT'S ONE SMALL STEP FOR DAN... ONE GIANT COW PIE WHEN I GET HOME!

AND WHEN HE LOOKED AROUND, THE MOON WAS COVERED IN CRITTERS!

YOU MEAN CRATERS, UNCLE DAN?

'NO - I MEAN CRITTERS! LOADS OF 'EM!'

GREETINGS! I COME IN PEACE.

BRICHTY
after BILL RITCHIE